Dot-to-Dot Mats

Publications International, Ltd.

Illustrations: Robin Boyer, Dani Jones, Chuck Whelon

Louis Weber, CEO
Publications International, Ltd.
7373 North Cicero Avenue
Lincolnwood, Illinois 60712

ISBN-13: 978-1-4508-2403-3
ISBN-10: 1-4508-2403-X

Manufactured in China.

8 7 6 5 4 3 2 1

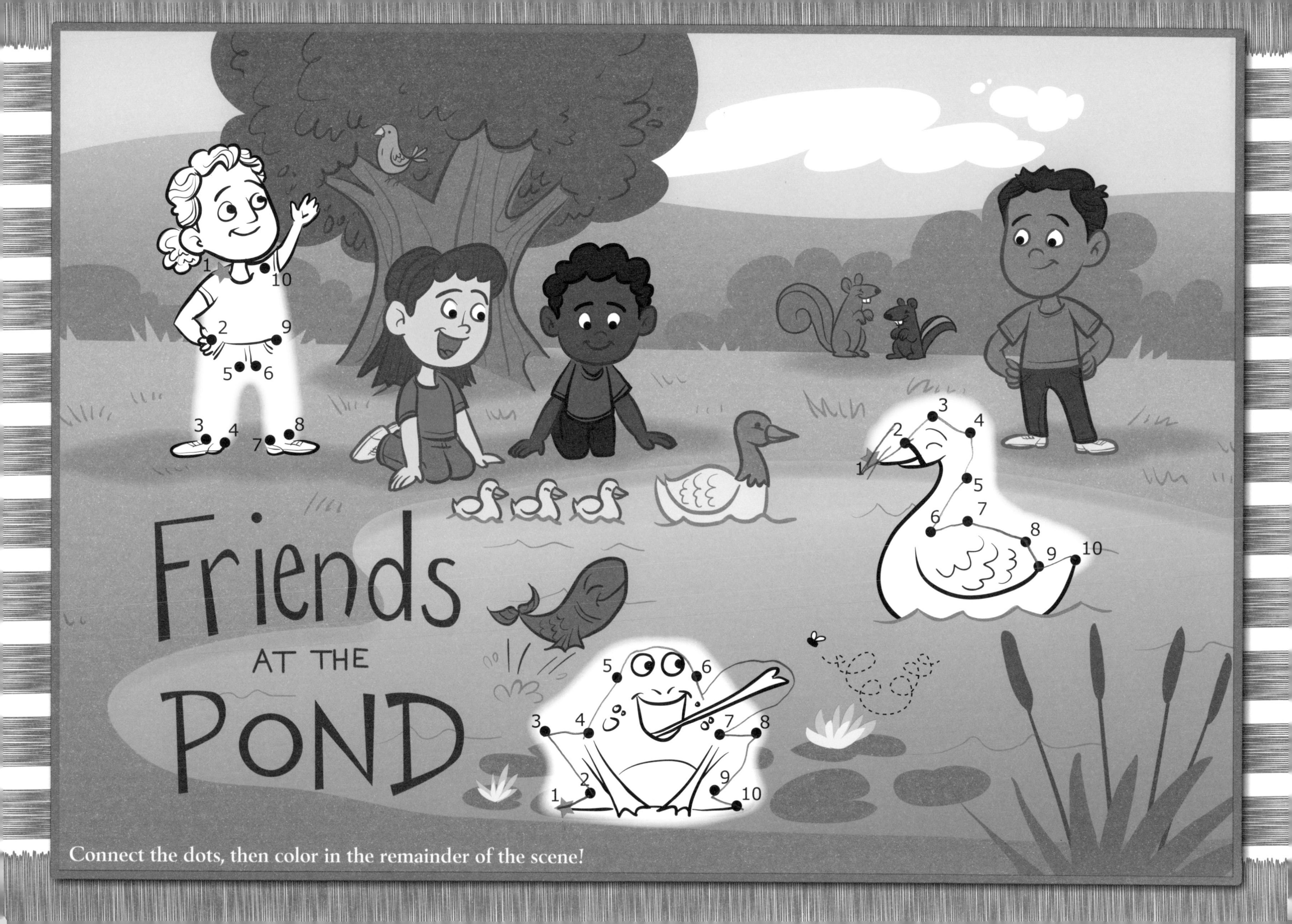
Friends
AT THE
POND
1
2
3
4
5
6
7
8
9
10
Connect the dots, then color in the remainder of the scene!

Time for Tea
Connect the dots, then color in the remainder of the scene!

Connect the dots, then color in the remainder of the scene!

At the
Grocery
Store
RUIT
N SALE
Connect the dots, then color in the remainder of the scene!

Plant a Garden
Connect the dots, then color in the remainder of the scene!

Bowling Fun
1
2
3
4
5
6
7
8
9
Connect the dots, then color in the remainder of the scene!

At the PETTING ZOO
Connect the dots, then color in the remainder of the scene!

NEED FOR SPEED
Connect the dots, then color in the remainder of the scene!

SPACED OUT
Connect the dots, then color in the remainder of the scene!

LET'S MAKE A PIZZA!
Connect the dots, then color in the remainder of the scene!

Go for the Goal!
Connect the dots, then color in the remainder of the scene!

ALIEN INTELLIGENCE
Connect the dots, then color in the remainder of the scene!

Time to Dine!
COLA
Connect the dots, then color in the remainder of the scene!

Fun AT THE Beach
Connect the dots, then color in the remainder of the scene!

MONSTER MAKER
Connect the dots, then color in the remainder of the scene!

At the
PET SHOP
Connect the dots, then color in the remainder of the scene!

POLAR PLAYTIME
Connect the dots, then color in the remainder of the scene!

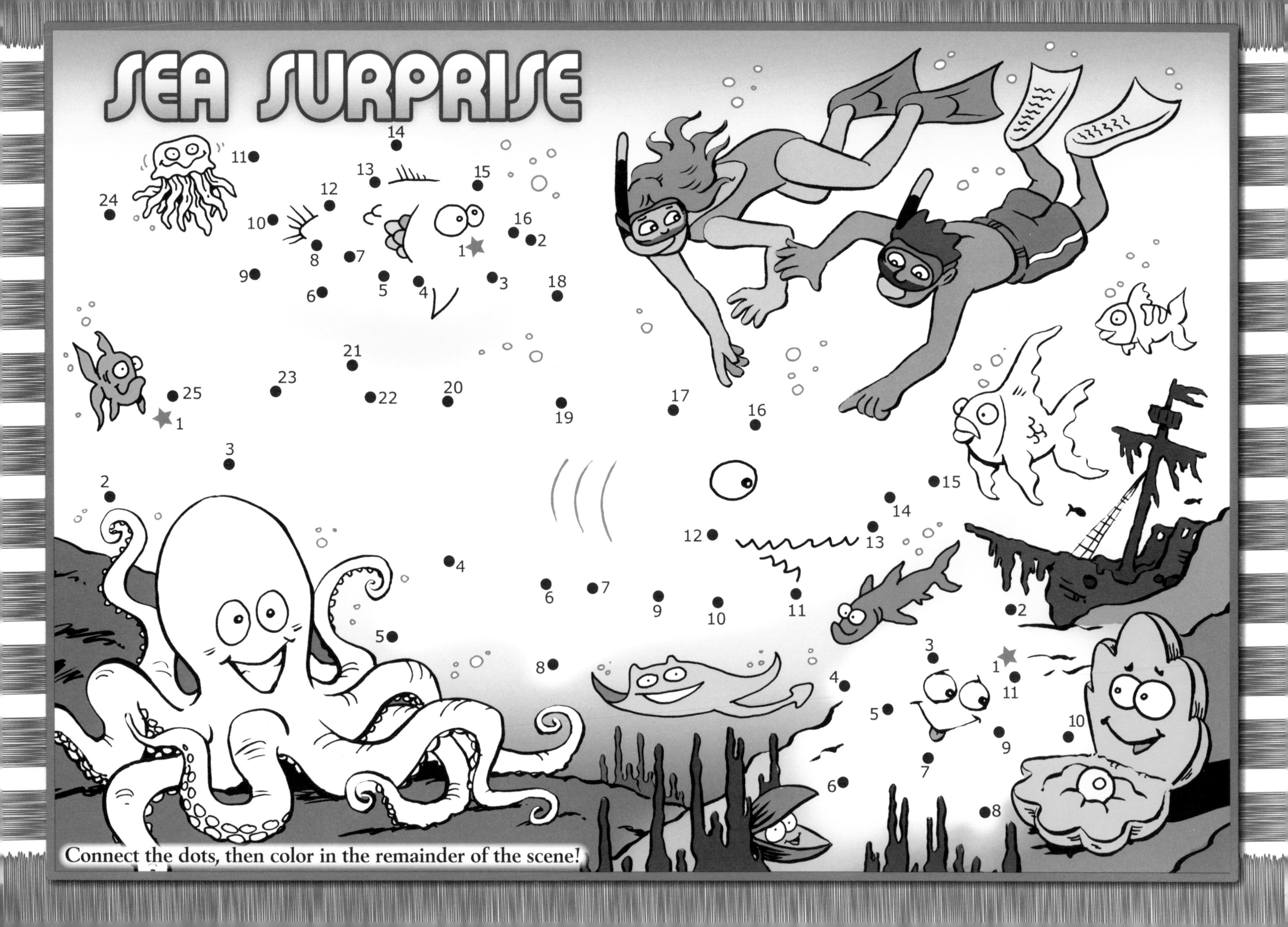
SEA SURPRISE
Connect the dots, then color in the remainder of the scene!

FUN AT THE
PARK
Connect the dots, then color in the remainder of the scene!

GOING UNDERGROUND
Connect the dots, then color in the remainder of the scene!

LIFE ON THE FARM
Connect the dots, then color in the remainder of the scene!

MUSEUMS ARE DINO-MITE!
All About Dinos
Connect the dots, then color in the remainder of the scene!

Pirate Puzzle
Connect the dots, then color in the remainder of the scene!

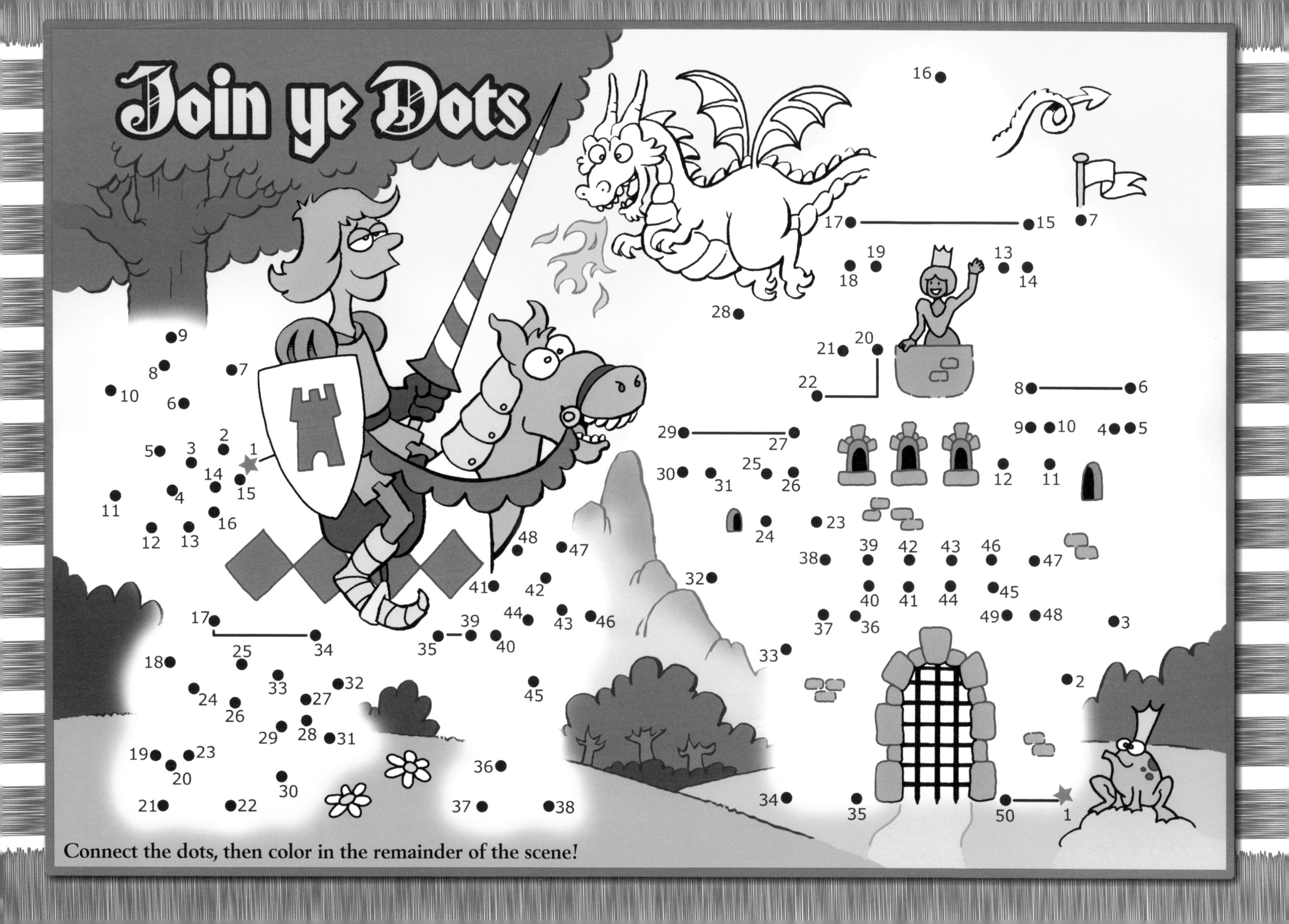
Join ye Dots
Connect the dots, then color in the remainder of the scene!

MUMMY MIA!
Connect the dots, then color in the remainder of the scene!

DOWNHILL RUN
Connect the dots, then color in the remainder of the scene!

JOIN THE DOTS
Connect the dots, then color in the remainder of the scene!

Sightseeing in Paris
CAFE
METRO
Monet
Connect the dots, then color in the remainder of the scene!

HOLIDAY CRUISE
Connect the dots, then color in the remainder of the scene!